Facts That Last
Addition

**A Balanced Approach
to Memorization**

Larry Leutzinger

Acknowledgments

Contributing Writers Janet Pittock, Jeffrey Stiegel

Editor Diane Nieker

Design Director Karen Lee Stack

Design Gerta Sorensen

Cover Illustration Amanda Haley

Illustrators Sarah Frederking, Amanda Haley

Production Carlisle Communications, Ltd.

ISBN 0-7622-1211-X

Customer Service 800-624-0822

www.creativepublications.com

3 4 5 6 7 8 ML 05 04 03 02

Contents

Introduction

The teaching of basic facts is an important component of any successful mathematics program. Many of the recommendations made by the National Council of Teachers of Mathematics (NCTM) in their *1989 Standards* assume children have fluency with basic operations. In its draft of *Standards 2000,* the NCTM clearly states that children need to memorize basic facts. Mastery of this information is necessary for developing both mental math and estimation skills. Many mathematical tasks become more efficient when basic facts can be recalled quickly and accurately.

In the past, teaching basic facts was often over-emphasized with too much time devoted to repetitive practice. The seven addition strategies presented in this book will help children remember their facts with a more appropriate amount of practice. The activities in *Facts That Last* provide the central portion of a successful three-step sequence for teaching basic fact mastery.

Having an understanding of number and the basic concepts of addition is the first step in the process of mastering the basic facts. (See prerequisites beginning on page vi.) The contents of this book address the second step—learning fact strategies to facilitate recall. Thirdly, children need to keep facts "fresh" with an appropriate amount of continuing practice. Practice can come from working on isolated facts or from working with facts embedded in more complex activities.

The strategies in this book demonstrate how to organize facts into groups that can be handled with generalizations. With this knowledge, the effort of learning each of 121 addition facts is reduced to the ease of remembering a handful of strategies. Mathematically powerful children often use many of these strategies naturally. When you encourage children in your class to use and discuss these strategies, you make that power available to your entire class!

The seven addition strategies included in this book are the commutative property, counting on, doubles, near doubles, sums of ten, adding ten, and making ten. See the next page for a chart listing the strategies.

Strategy Chart

Commutative Property

Any two addends always equal the same sum, no matter what their order.

$2 + 3 = 3 + 2$

Count on

When you add 0, 1, 2, or 3, count on from the other number.

$6 + 3$ is 7, 8, 9, so $6 + 3 = 9$.

$6 + 7$ 8 9

Doubles

Doubles are easy to remember.

Near Doubles

To find "near doubles," count on from doubles.

$3 + 5$ is $6 + 2$ or 8, so $3 + 5 = 8$.

+2

Sums of Ten

When you think of adding to make ten, think of completing a pair of hands or a ten-frame.

Adding Ten

When you add a ten to a number, you just add one to the tens place.

$3 + 10 = 13$.

10¢ 1¢ 1¢ 1¢

Making Ten

Sometimes it helps to break up the numbers to make a ten. Then add on the leftovers.

$8 + 5 = 8 + 2 + 3 = 10 + 3 = 13$, so $8 + 5 = 13$.

$8 + 5 = 13$

How This Book Is Organized

How to Use This Book

Facts That Last combines lessons presenting the strategies and practice children need to memorize their facts. You may choose to supplement or replace the work in your mathematics textbook with this material. You may choose to use the entire book, or just the strategies your children need most.

Teaching Sequence

First determine that your children are ready to memorize. The prerequisites chart (pages viii-1) lists evidences of readiness. Should you conclude that children are not ready, you'll find suggested activities and resources listed in the prerequisite chart.

At the beginning of each strategy section you'll find an overview which provides a summary of the strategy, prerequisites specific to that strategy, information about when to use the strategy, and additional strategy-related experiences for your students. You'll also find references to the optional practice book.

Every strategy section starts with warm-ups. Warm-ups include introductory experiences, mental math experiences, and a refreshing of the

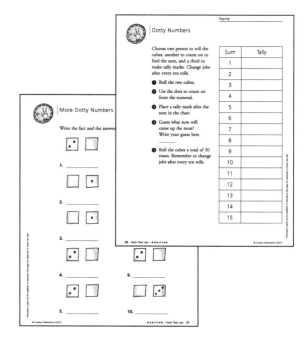

skills children need for the strategy. These warm-ups are designed to take three to five minutes. Some strategy sections have five warm-ups while others have ten. Many teachers enjoy using these warm-ups during the transition time between activities or when children are lining up.

Next comes an activity that helps children gain an understanding of why the strategy is useful and when to appropriately apply it. The activity provides experience and practice with the strategy. Activities may be done as a whole class, in cooperative groups, or individually. Each activity takes at least one class period.

The third component of each strategy section is practice. Practices are similar in format and feel to the warm-ups. The focus of practice is to use the strategy to recall facts quickly and correctly.

Once the children in your class have memorized their addition facts, you can help them to gain quick and accurate recall by providing engaging ways to practice those facts. See the bibliography (page 88) for more complete information about suggested resources.

Talk About It

Children who talk about their own thinking and hear how other children think become stronger at using strategies. You'll find hints for leading discourse about children's thinking throughout the book. Often, questions for a class discussion will appear at the beginning of a set of warm ups or practice pages. These questions are designed to be used throughout the warm up or practice period. You'll also find questions embedded in activities that ask children to describe their thinking.

Materials

Teacher notes found at the beginning of activities, warm-ups, and practice sets, tell you what supplies are needed for the activity. The items listed, however, are by no means the only materials that can be used. If you don't have the specific equipment named, use alternative materials that are available to you. Materials lists for some of the activities offer suggestions for alternatives.

The following is a list of all of the materials suggested for use with activities in this book.

▶ One set of 101 number cards, numbered from 0 to 100. Numbers should be large enough for all children to see.

▶ One set of 121 addition flash cards, including facts from 0 + 0 to 10 + 10.

▶ Twenty (20) LinkerCubes® for each child

▶ Two blank number cubes for each group of three children

▶ One blank spinner for each pair of children

▶ One GeoMirror for each pair of children

Additional Materials

The following materials are needed for the additional experiences described in the overviews. Feel free to use alternative materials.

▶ Twenty (20) clothespins

▶ Posterboard

▶ Modeling clay, a fist-sized piece for each child

▶ Six pipe cleaners for each child

▶ Twenty (20) birthday candles, ten (10) each of two colors for each child

▶ Brown paper bags, one for each group of four children

▶ 0-99 chart for each child

▶ One dime and eighteen (18) pennies for each child

Prerequisites

Research has shown that children with a solid conceptual foundation are more successful when they begin memorizing their facts. The following chart summarizes key concepts your students should fully understand before they are asked to memorize. If your children own the concepts listed in the first column of the chart, they are ready to begin successfully committing their facts to memory. However, if you determine that your students need more experiences before they begin the activities in this book, you might start with the suggestions offered in the second column of the chart. Additional activities can be found in the resources listed in the third column. A bibliography is located on page 88.

Key Concepts

Children explain that addition is putting items together. They can model addition problems with cubes or other manipulatives.

Children employ various methods to arrive at correct sums for addition fact exercises. Methods may include counting on fingers, using manipulatives, counting on, and relating the exercise to one that is similar and using number sense to find the unknown answer.

Children understand relationships of numbers from 0 to 20. Given two numbers under 20, they immediately know which number is greater than or less than the other.

Children can construct and deconstruct numbers. They demonstrate that 1 + 3, 1 + 1 + 2, and 2 + 2 are all equal in value to 4.

Children have an intuitive understanding of the commutative property of addition. Children can match facts with the same addends in different order without having to find the sums. They can explain that $x + y$ has the same answer as $y + x$. After finding a sum, for example 4 + 9, they can immediately tell the answer for 9 + 4.

Activities to Provide More Experiences	Recommended Resources
First have children create trains by linking two colors of LinkerCubes®. Then ask children to describe their trains with addition sentences.	*Constructing Ideas About Number Combinations* by Sandra Ward. *Understanding Addition & Subtraction* by Linda Holden and Micaelia Randolph Brummett.
Provide experiences for children to find answers to addition exercises. In whole class discussions, encourage children to tell how they figure out answers when they do not have facts memorized.	*Smart Arithmetic, Grades 1-3* by Rhea Irvine and Kathryn Walker.
Tell children two numbers and have them point to the numbers on a number line. Ask children to tell you which number is greater. For another pair of numbers, have children tell you which is less. 	*Smart Arithmetic, Grades 1-3* by Rhea Irvine and Kathryn Walker.
Ask children to use counters to demonstrate many ways to show a number.	*Constructing Ideas About Number Combinations* by Sandra Ward.
Use manipulatives to model an addition fact. Ask children to tell you two different ways of stating the addition fact.	*Constructing Ideas About Number Combinations* by Sandra Ward.

Commutative Property Strategy Overview

What is the Commutative Property Strategy?

You know that addition is commutative—that the order in which addends are combined does not change the sum. The knowledge that $3 + 8 = 8 + 3$ helps children cut the number of facts they need to memorize by nearly half. Many children know this intuitively, but talking about it helps all children utilize this property as a powerful strategy for remembering addition facts.

You will notice the warm-ups include some extensions that reveal not all operations are commutative. This prepares students for the idea that while the commutative property applies to addition, not all operations are commutative. Just as knowing that order matters when putting on socks and shoes—putting shoes on before socks yields a different result from putting socks on before shoes—it will be important for children to know that subtraction is not commutative.

When to Use the Commutative Property Strategy

This strategy can be used with any addition fact. When a child learns an addition fact, the sum for a second fact that has the same addends in reverse order can easily be recalled by applying the commutative property.

+	0	1	2	3	4	5	6	7	8	9	10
0	0	1	2	3	4	5	6	7	8	9	10
1	1	2	3	4	5	6	7	8	9	10	11
2	2	3	4	5	6	7	8	9	10	11	12
3	3	4	5	6	7	8	9	10	11	12	13
4	4	5	6	7	8	9	10	11	12	13	14
5	5	6	7	8	9	10	11	12	13	14	15
6	6	7	8	9	10	11	12	13	14	15	16
7	7	8	9	10	11	12	13	14	15	16	17
8	8	9	10	11	12	13	14	15	16	17	18
9	9	10	11	12	13	14	15	16	17	18	19
10	10	11	12	13	14	15	16	17	18	19	20

Prerequisites

Children should understand addition concepts (page viii). They should be able to understand the thinking required to apply the commutative property as a strategy for memorizing their facts.

Additional Experiences

Put a number of clothespins along one side of a piece of posterboard and another number along the opposite side. Ask the children to write the number sentence that tells how many clothespins there are in all (for example, 4 + 3 = 7). Rotate the posterboard 180° so the clothespins appear to switch sides. Ask the children to write the number sentence that tells how many there are now (in our example, 3 + 4 = 7). Have them write the second number sentence just below the first. Try more examples. Discuss the pattern with your class.

Additional practice can be found in *Fact Practice Workbooks, Levels 1-5,* by Creative Publications, Inc.

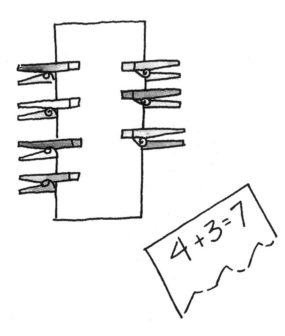

Commutative Property Strategy

Warm-Ups

Each warm-up exercise set should take two (2) or three (3) minutes. The short exercise sets are great for filling transition times. Some teachers use them while children stand in line.

Talk About It

As the children work through these warm-ups, ask them to talk about their thinking. This not only helps you assess, but gives children a chance to clarify their thinking and to hear about ways of thinking that might be different from theirs. You might ask questions like

How did you know the answer so quickly?
(Answers will vary.)

Why is this strategy useful?
(Applying this strategy reduces the number of facts that need to be learned.)

A great question to keep the discussion going is

Did anyone use a different way to find the answer?

Day 1

Ask children for the correct sum.

4 + 1 (5)
1 + 4 (5)
9 + 1 (10)
1 + 9 (10)
7 + 1 (8)
1 + 7 (8)

Continue asking children for sums when adding 1 to numbers 0 through 10.

Extension Ask children for sums when adding 1 to numbers 0 through 99.

Day 2

Ask children for the correct sum.

4 + 2 (6)
2 + 4 (6)
9 + 2 (11)
2 + 9 (11)
7 + 2 (9)
2 + 7 (9)

Continue asking children for sums when adding 2 to numbers 0 through 10.

Extension Ask children for sums when adding 2 to numbers 0 through 98.

Day 3

Ask children for the correct sum.

4 + 3 (7)

3 + 4 (7)

9 + 3 (12)

3 + 9 (12)

7 + 3 (10)

3 + 7 (10)

Continue asking children for sums when adding 3 to numbers 0 through 10.

Extension Ask children for sums when adding 3 to numbers 0 through 97.

Day 4

Ask children for a fact that is sure to give the same sum.

1 + 8 (8 + 1)

2 + 5 (5 + 2)

1 + 6 (6 + 1)

3 + 8 (8 + 3)

2 + 7 (7 + 2)

3 + 6 (6 + 3)

Continue asking children for sums when adding 1, 2, or 3 to numbers 0 through 10.

Extension Ask children for sums when adding 1, 2, or 3 to numbers 0 through 97.

Day 5

Ask children for another fact that has the same addends and is sure to give the same sum.

4 + 8 (8 + 4)

5 + 11 (11 + 5)

2 + 13 (13 + 2)

7 + 14 (14 + 7)

6 + 10 (10 + 6)

3 + 15 (15 + 3)

Continue asking children for sums when adding a one-digit number to numbers 0 through 90.

Extension Ask children for sums when adding an "unknown number" to other numbers through 20. (For example, 5 + "unknown number" = "unknown number" + 5.)

Topsy Turvy

Individual Activity

Summary

Children build two-color trains using from two (2) to twenty (20) LinkerCubes®. They write the fact that describes the train from left to right, then flip the train and write the related fact.

Materials

Each child needs

▶ A copy of Topsy Turvy, page 8

▶ Twenty (20) LinkerCubes®, ten each of two colors

---

notes When making their trains, children need to keep cubes of the same color grouped together so that the train can be described with exactly two addends.

Once children have the idea that the order of combination does not change the sum, you might choose to introduce them to the mathematical name of that property—commutative property of addition. You might think "commutative" is too big for younger students, but many of them really like to collect large words. Remember—this is the group that knows the names of dozens of dinosaurs!

Children may choose a "doubles" combination when they make their own trains as they complete page 9. With doubles, both addends are the same, so they yield only one fact. The challenge on page 9 focuses children's attention on this special kind of fact.

Directions

❶ Show children how to use their LinkerCubes® to model 3 + 5 = 8.

❷ Ask children to make a train starting with three cubes of one color, then adding five cubes of the other color.

❸ Have children tell you what addition fact the train represents. Write the fact (3 + 5 = 8) on the board.

❹ Instruct students to flip the train so that the colors switch sides. Ask them to tell you what fact this train represents (5 + 3 = 8). Write the fact on the board.

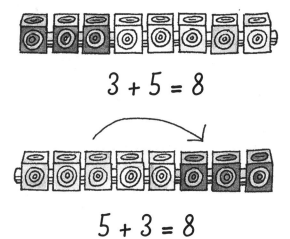

$$3 + 5 = 8$$

$$5 + 3 = 8$$

❺ Repeat with a few different facts until students are comfortable making trains and telling related facts.

❻ Have children complete Topsy Turvy, page 8, and then allow children an opportunity to discuss their findings.

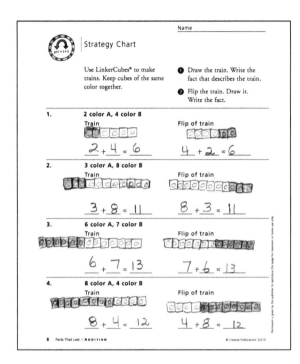

What did you notice about the two facts for each train?

(The sum is always the same; the order in which you add the numbers does not matter. Accept other accurate observations.)

So, if I tell you that 6 + 8 = 14, put your hand up when you know what 8 + 6 is.

(Once most hands are up, ask children to tell you the answer.)

How do you know?

(Accept all valid responses. This is a good opportunity to assess which children are using the commutative property.)

So, if 24 + 36 = 60, what is 36 + 24?

(60)

How do you know?

(Again, accept all valid responses. Allow children to elaborate on using the commutative property.)

Extension

Make a copy of Have It Both Ways, page 9, for each child. Have children create two-color trains using up to twenty (20) LinkerCubes®. For each train made, children should record the addition fact, flip the train, and record the fact for the flip.

Topsy Turvy

Use LinkerCubes® to make trains. Keep cubes of the same color together.

1 Draw the train. Write the fact that describes the train.

2 Flip the train. Draw it. Write the fact.

---

1. **2 color A, 4 color B**

Train

Flip of train

____ + ____ = _____   ____ + ____ = _____

---

2. **3 color A, 8 color B**

Train

Flip of train

____ + ____ = _____   ____ + ____ = _____

---

3. **6 color A, 7 color B**

Train

Flip of train

____ + ____ = _____   ____ + ____ = _____

---

4. **8 color A, 4 color B**

Train

Flip of train

____ + ____ = _____   ____ + ____ = _____

Have it Both Ways

Build LinkerCube® trains. Use two colors for each train. Write the fact. Then flip the train and write another addition fact.

Extra Challenge Find trains you can describe with only ONE fact. Write those facts on the back of this page. Then, explain how you know when there will be only one addition fact that describes a train.

1. ___ + ___ = _____   ___ + ___ = _____

2. ___ + ___ = _____   ___ + ___ = _____

3. ___ + ___ = _____   ___ + ___ = _____

4. ___ + ___ = _____   ___ + ___ = _____

5. ___ + ___ = _____   ___ + ___ = _____

6. ___ + ___ = _____   ___ + ___ = _____

7. ___ + ___ = _____   ___ + ___ = _____

8. ___ + ___ = _____   ___ + ___ = _____

9. ___ + ___ = _____   ___ + ___ = _____

10. ___ + ___ = _____   ___ + ___ = _____

Commutative Property Strategy

Practice

Work on these sets of practice exercises until children get each answer within three (3) seconds. Ask children to state the entire fact rather than just the answer ("2 + 3 = 3 + 2," instead of "3 + 2"). Stating the complete fact improves students' recall. Present the facts in various ways. Ask the children to listen and then reply verbally, or use flash cards and have the children write their facts. Varying the format helps all children focus on the facts.

Talk About It

Ask children to talk about their thinking. Follow up by asking if anyone has a different way to find the answer.

What do you notice about the sum when addends are switched around?
(The sum is the same.)

Why doesn't the order of the addends matter in an addition fact?
(The same amounts are being put together.)

Can you think of two numbers that give a different sum when switched?
(No.)

Day 1

Ask children to give another fact that is sure to have the same sum because it has the same addends, and have them include the sum in their answer.

7 + 1 (7 + 1 = 8)
4 + 1 (1 + 4 = 5)
2 + 1 (1 + 2 = 3)
10 + 1 (1 + 10 = 11)
5 + 1 (1 + 5 = 6)
0 + 1 (1 + 0 = 1)
9 + 1 (1 + 9 = 10)
3 + 1 (1 + 3 = 4)
6 + 1 (1 + 6 = 7)

Extension Have children add 1 to any number less than 99, then reverse the addends.

....

Day 2

Follow directions for Day 1.

7 + 2 (2 + 7 = 9)
4 + 2 (2 + 4 = 6)
8 + 2 (2 + 8 = 10)
10 + 2 (2 + 10 = 12)
5 + 2 (2 + 5 = 7)
0 + 2 (2 + 0 = 2)
9 + 2 (2 + 9 = 11)
3 + 2 (2 + 3 = 5)
6 + 2 (2 + 6 = 8)

Extension Have children add 2 to any number less than 98, then reverse the addends.

Day 3

Ask children to give another fact that is sure to have the same sum because it has the same addends, and have them include the sum in their answer.

7 + 3 (3 + 7 = 10)

4 + 3 (3 + 4 = 7)

8 + 3 (3 + 8 = 11)

10 + 3 (3 + 10 = 13)

5 + 3 (3 + 5 = 8)

0 + 3 (3 + 0 = 3)

9 + 3 (3 + 9 = 12)

1 + 3 (3 + 1 = 4)

6 + 3 (3 + 6 = 9)

Extension Have children add 3 to any number less than 97, then reverse the addends.

Day 4

Follow directions for Day 3.

2 + 6	(6 + 2 = 8)	1 + 5	(5 + 1 = 6)
1 + 8	(8 + 1 = 9)	2 + 4	(4 + 2 = 6)
0 + 5	(5 + 0 = 5)	3 + 5	(5 + 3 = 8)
3 + 9	(9 + 3 = 12)	0 + 4	(4 + 0 = 4)
1 + 4	(4 + 1 = 5)	2 + 9	(9 + 2 = 11)
2 + 3	(3 + 2 = 5)	3 + 7	(7 + 3 = 10)
0 + 8	(8 + 0 = 8)	2 + 5	(5 + 2 = 7)
2 + 7	(7 + 2 = 9)	1 + 9	(9 + 1 = 10)
3 + 10	(10 + 3 = 13)	2 + 10	(10 + 2 = 12)

Extension Ask children for sums when adding 0, 1, 2, or 3 to numbers greater than 10. Have children give the new fact and the sum.

Day 5

Follow directions for Day 3.

5 + 9	(9 + 5 = 14)	6 + 7	(7 + 6 = 13)
4 + 10	(10 + 4 = 14)	5 + 10	(10 + 5 = 15)
3 + 7	(7 + 3 = 10)	7 + 8	(8 + 7 = 15)
6 + 8	(8 + 6 = 14)	4 + 8	(8 + 4 = 12)
7 + 9	(9 + 7 =16)	3 + 6	(6 + 3 = 9)
4 + 5	(5 + 4 = 9)	2 + 8	(8 + 2 = 10)
1 + 6	(6 + 1 = 7)	0 + 10	(10 + 0 = 10)
4 + 9	(9 + 4 = 13)	4 + 7	(7 + 4 = 11)
3 + 8	(8 + 3 = 11)	5 + 8	(8 + 5 = 13)

Extension Ask children for sums when single-digit numbers are added to numbers greater than 10.

Count-on Strategy Overview

What Is the Count-on Strategy?

Most children naturally use the count-on strategy when they begin to add. In its most efficient use, children start with the larger of the addends, and count on the number indicated by the smaller addend. For example, 7 + 3, start at 7 and count on "8, 9, 10." So, 7 + 3 = 10.

Counting on is a vital skill for all children. It provides the foundation for learning certain addition facts such as those involving adding 0, 1, 2, or 3.

When to Use Count-on Strategy

The count-on strategy is best used with facts that require adding 0, 1, 2, or 3.

+	0	1	2	3	4	5	6	7	8	9	10
0	0	1	2	3	4	5	6	7	8	9	10
1	1	2	3	4	5	6	7	8	9	10	11
2	2	3	4	5	6	7	8	9	10	11	12
3	3	4	5	6	7	8	9	10	11	12	13
4	4	5	6	7							
5	5	6	7	8							
6	6	7	8	9							
7	7	8	9	10							
8	8	9	10	11							
9	9	10	11	12							
10	10	11	12	13							

Prerequisites

Children should understand addition concepts (page viii). They should also be able to count on from any number less than twenty.

Additional Experiences

Children play "Count on Guess and Check" in pairs. Pairs agree that they are adding 0, 1, 2, or 3. One child says a number. The second child must immediately tell the sum of that number plus the addend agreed on. The two children count on together to verify the sum. After three turns, the children switch roles.

Additional practice can be found in *Fact Practice Workbooks, Levels 1-5,* by Creative Publications, Inc.

Count-on Strategy

Warm-Ups

Each warm-up exercise set should take two (2) or three (3) minutes. The short problem sets are great for filling transition times. Some teachers use them while children stand in line.

Materials

Number Cards, 0-100. Each card should be large enough to be seen by all children when displayed to the class. (If you do not have cards, you may write numbers for each problem on the chalkboard or overhead projector.)

Talk About It

As children work through these warm-ups, ask them to talk about their thinking. This not only helps you assess, but gives children a chance to clarify their thinking and to hear about ways of thinking that might be different from their own. You might ask questions like

How do you keep track of numbers as you count on to be sure you count the right number?
(Accept all valid methods.)

How do you know what number to begin counting on from? (Count on from the larger addend.)

A great question to keep the discussion going is

Does anyone have a different way to find the answer?

Day 1

Say the next three numbers.
2, 3, 4, . . . (5, 6, 7)

Say the next three numbers.
5, 6, 7, . . . (8, 9, 10)

Say the next three numbers.
7, 8, 9, . . . (10, 11, 12)

Continue saying three (3) numbers starting at less than eleven (11).

Extension Say any three (3) consecutive numbers less than 96. Have children say the next three numbers.

Day 2

When you count, what number comes after 7?
(8)

When you count, what number comes after 4?
(5)

When you count, what number comes after 8?
(9)

Ask children to tell what counting number comes after any number, 1 through 10.

Extension Ask children to tell what counting number comes after any number, 0 through 98.

Day 3
Hold up a number card, such as 7.

What is the next number?
(8)

Hold up number cards from 1 through 10 in random order, each time asking children what number comes next.

Extension Hold up any number card from 0 through 98 and ask children what number comes next.

Day 4
Hold up a number card, such as 8.

Count on 1 from 8.
(9)

Hold up 7
Count on 2 from 7.
(8, 9)

Hold up 5
Count on 2 from 5.
(6, 7)

Continue asking children to count on 2 from any number card, 1 through 10.

Extension Have children count on 2 from any number card, 0 through 97.

Day 5

Hold up a number card, such as 8.

Count on 2 from 8.

(9,10)

Have children continue counting on 1 or 2 from any number, 1 through 10.

Extension Have children count on 1 or 2 from any number less than 98.

Day 6

Hold up a number card, such as 6.

Count on 2 from 6.

(7, 8)

Ask children to count on 1 or 2 from any number less than 11.

Extension Ask children to count on 1 or 2 from any number less than 97.

Day 7

Hold up a number card, such as 4.

Count on 2 from 4.

(5, 6)

Ask children to count on 1 or 2 from any number card, 1 through 11.

Extension Ask children to count on 1 or 2 starting with any number card from 0 through 97.

Day 8
Hold up a number card, such as 8.

Count on 3 from 8.
(9, 10, 11)

Ask children to count on 3 from any number card, 1 through 11.

Extension Have children count on 3 from any number card, 0 through 97.

Day 9

Count on 3 from 5.
(6, 7, 8)

Count on 3 from 7.
(8, 9, 10)

Count on 3 from 9.
(10, 11, 12)

Ask children to count on 3 from any number, 1 through 11.

Extension Have children count on 3 from any number less than 97.

Day 10
Ask children to count on 1, 2, or 3 from any number, 1 through 10.

Extension Have children count on 1, 2, or 3 from any number less than 97.

Dotty Numbers

Summary

Children roll number cubes and dot cubes to generate count-on activities for practice.

Small Group Activity

Materials

Each group of 3 children needs

▶ A copy of Dotty Numbers, page 20

▶ A copy of More Dotty Numbers, page 21

▶ A number cube with the numerals 4, 5, 6, 7, 8, and 9.

▶ A dot cube with 1, 1, 2, 2, 3, and 3 dots.

While children roll cubes, draw a large version of the tally chart found on page 20 on the chalkboard.

Directions

❶ One child rolls the cubes, another determines the sum by counting on, and the third records the sum with a tally mark after the proper number on the tally sheet. The children change roles after every 10 rolls of the cubes.

❷ After each group completes rolling the cubes 30 times, they record the group's tallies onto the large chart on the chalkboard. Encourage children to make tally marks in fives when recording their results.

❸ When all of the groups have recorded their tallies, ask the children to count the number of tally marks after each sum. Have children compare the numbers and determine which sums occur more often than others.

❹ Discuss the ideas of probability and chance with your class. Ask the children to compare the frequencies of their group's results with those recorded on the class tally and tell how they differ. (There might be a small variation or a large one, all dependent on chance.)

Why are the results for each group different?

(Because the cubes roll differently for each group.)

Which group is right?

(All the groups are right; the tallies illustrate chance and probability.)

Extension or Homework

Make a copy of More Dotty Numbers, page 21, and write numerals on the blank cube faces. Use this copy as a master to make copies for your entire class.

Alternatively, make copies without filling in the blank cube faces. Then children can create their own exercises by filling in the cube faces themselves.

notes

Probability and Chance in Dotty Numbers

The theoretical probability of rolling each sum:

Sum	Theoretical probability
5	2/36 or 1/18
6	4/36 or 1/9
7	6/36 or 1/6
8	6/36 or 1/6
9	6/36 or 1/6
10	6/36 or 1/6
11	4/36 or 1/9
12	2/36 or 1/18

You can find the theoretical probability by finding all the possible cube combinations and how often each combination occurs.

In this activity, your children are finding the experimental probability—the actual occurrence of the totals in thirty (30) trials per group.

Note that while the tally chart on page 20 has spaces to record sums from 1 through 15, the only sums possible are 5 through 12. The probability of throwing a sum less than five or greater than twelve is zero (0). This is an interesting point for discussion.

Dotty Numbers

Choose one person to roll the cubes, another to count on to find the sum, and a third to make tally marks. Change jobs after every ten rolls.

1 Roll the two cubes.

2 Use the dots to count on from the numeral.

3 Place a tally mark after the sum in the chart.

4 Guess what sum will come up the most? Write your guess here.

_____

5 Roll the cubes a total of 30 times. Remember to change jobs after every ten rolls.

Sum	Tally
1	
2	
3	
4	
5	
6	
7	
8	
9	
10	
11	
12	
13	
14	
15	

More Dotty Numbers

Write the fact and the answer.

1. _____   **2.** _____

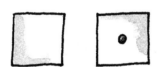   

3. _____   **4.** _____

5. _____   **6.** _____

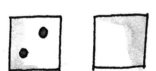

7. _____   **8.** _____

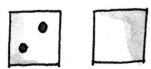

9. _____   **10.** _____

Count-on Strategy

Practice

Work on these sets of practice exercises until children get each answer within three (3) seconds. Ask children to state the entire fact rather than just the answer ("2 + 3 = 5" instead of "5"). Stating the complete fact improves students' recall. Present the facts in various ways. Ask the children to listen and then reply verbally, or use flash cards and have the children write their facts. Varying the format helps all children focus on the facts.

Talk About It

Ask children to talk about their thinking. Follow up by asking if anyone has a different way to find the answer.

What do you know about adding zero?
(Any number plus zero is that number.)

Why does that rule work?
(Because zero means "none.")

What do you know about adding one?
(The answer is the next counting number.)

What do you know about adding two?
(You count on two. If you start with an even number, you get the next even number. If you start with an odd number, you get the next odd number.)

What do you know about adding three?
(You count on three. Some children may have other valid methods.)

Day 1

Present these facts.

7 + 1 (8)	8 + 1 (9)
1 + 6 (7)	1 + 4 (5)
9 + 1 (10)	0 + 1 (1)
1 + 7 (8)	1 + 8 (9)
2 + 1 (3)	6 + 1 (7)
4 + 1 (5)	5 + 1 (6)
1 + 2 (3)	1 + 3 (4)
1 + 1 (2)	1 + 0 (1)
1 + 5 (6)	2 + 0 (2)
7 + 1 (8)	

Extension Ask children to give sums when adding 1 to any number through 98.

Day 2

Present these facts.

6 + 0 (6)	0 + 4 (4)
9 + 1 (10)	1 + 5 (6)
1 + 7 (8)	1 + 9 (10)
4 + 1 (5)	1 + 3 (4)
0 + 7 (7)	1 + 6 (7)
1 + 8 (9)	6 + 1 (7)
8 + 0 (8)	0 + 3 (3)
3 + 1 (4)	0 + 9 (9)
0 + 6 (6)	8 + 1 (9)
1 + 1 (2)	5 + 1 (6)

Extension Ask children to give sums when adding 0 or 1 to any number less than 100.

Day 3

Present these facts.

7 + 2 (9)	9 + 2 (11)
6 + 2 (8)	1 + 5 (6)
2 + 9 (11)	2 + 7 (9)
8 + 2 (10)	7 + 1 (8)
4 + 2 (6)	2 + 8 (10)
2 + 6 (8)	2 + 5 (7)
8 + 1 (9)	2 + 3 (5)
5 + 2 (7)	6 + 1 (7)
2 + 9 (11)	0 + 2 (2)
3 + 2 (5)	9 + 1 (10)

Extension Ask children to give sums when adding 1 or 2 to any number less than 100.

Day 4

Present these facts.

2 + 4 (6)	8 + 2 (10)
4 + 1 (5)	2 + 9 (11)
1 + 4 (5)	2 + 2 (4)
2 + 8 (10)	1 + 2 (3)
4 + 2 (6)	9 + 2 (11)
2 + 0 (2)	2 + 7 (9)
5 + 2 (7)	3 + 2 (5)
6 + 2 (8)	1 + 0 (1)
2 + 5 (7)	7 + 2 (9)
2 + 6 (8)	7 + 1 (8)

Extension Ask children to give sums when adding 1 or 2 to any number less than 100.

Day 5

Present these facts.

6 + 2 (8)	5 + 1 (6)
4 + 2 (6)	7 + 2 (9)
2 + 9 (11)	1 + 4 (5)
9 + 1 (10)	5 + 2 (7)
8 + 2 (10)	9 + 2 (11)
2 + 4 (6)	2 + 3 (5)
1 + 8 (9)	2 + 2 (4)
7 + 1 (8)	2 + 7 (9)
2 + 6 (8)	2 + 0 (2)
3 + 1 (4)	2 + 1 (3)

Extension Ask children to give sums when adding 1 or 2 to any number less than 100.

Day 6

Present these facts.

0 + 5 (5)	2 + 5 (7)
9 + 0 (9)	7 + 0 (7)
2 + 8 (10)	8 + 0 (8)
1 + 6 (7)	5 + 0 (5)
8 + 2 (10)	5 + 2 (7)
3 + 0 (3)	1 + 7 (8)
6 + 2 (8)	8 + 1 (9)
4 + 0 (4)	1 + 2 (3)
2 + 4 (6)	7 + 2 (9)
1 + 3 (4)	1 + 9 (10)

Extension Ask children to give sums when adding 1 or 2 to any number less than 100.

Day 7

Present these facts.

4 + 2 (6)	8 + 2 (10)
6 + 2 (8)	9 + 2 (11)
2 + 3 (5)	6 + 1 (7)
3 + 5 (8)	3 + 8 (11)
3 + 3 (6)	2 + 5 (7)
4 + 3 (7)	8 + 3 (11)
6 + 3 (9)	9 + 3 (12)
1 + 8 (9)	7 + 3 (10)
1 + 6 (7)	9 + 1 (10)
3 + 9 (12)	5 + 3 (8)

Extension Ask children to give sums when adding 1 or 2, or 3 to any number less than 100.

Day 8

Present these facts.

3 + 6 (9)	2 + 9 (11)
1 + 7 (8)	4 + 3 (7)
2 + 4 (6)	1 + 2 (3)
0 + 7 (7)	7 + 3 (10)
6 + 3 (9)	3 + 4 (7)
8 + 3 (11)	5 + 3 (8)
0 + 8 (8)	3 + 7 (10)
3 + 5 (8)	2 + 8 (10)
3 + 8 (11)	1 + 5 (6)
1 + 9 (10)	9 + 3 (12)

Extension Ask children to give sums when adding 1, 2, or 3 to any number less than 100.

Day 9

Present these facts.

9 + 3 (12)	3 + 4 (7)
0 + 4 (4)	2 + 1 (3)
3 + 7 (10)	3 + 3 (6)
0 + 9 (9)	8 + 3 (11)
3 + 6 (9)	7 + 3 (10)
2 + 6 (8)	2 + 2 (4)
0 + 0 (0)	6 + 3 (9)
1 + 4 (5)	3 + 9 (12)
5 + 1 (6)	3 + 5 (8)
8 + 0 (8)	2 + 0 (2)

Extension Ask children to give sums when adding 1, 2, or 3 to any number less than 100.

Day 10

Present these facts.

3 + 7 (10)	3 + 4 (7)
3 + 1 (4)	2 + 7 (9)
3 + 8 (11)	5 + 3 (8)
3 + 6 (9)	0 + 1 (1)
0 + 3 (3)	8 + 1 (9)
0 + 6 (6)	3 + 9 (12)
8 + 3 (11)	6 + 3 (9)
3 + 0 (3)	9 + 3 (12)
9 + 0 (9)	7 + 3 (10)
3 + 3 (6)	7 + 0 (7)

Extension Ask children to give sums when adding 1, 2, or 3 to any number less than 100.

Doubles Strategy Overview

What is the Doubles Strategy?

Most children naturally remember doubles. This strategy builds on their natural ability to remember doubles by providing mental images of the doubles.

When to Use the Doubles Strategy

The doubles strategy is used with addition facts in which both addends are the same.

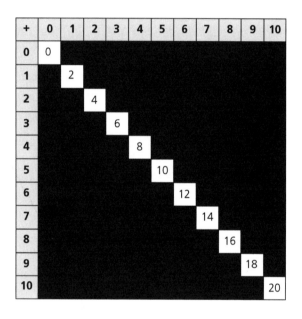

Prerequisites

Children should understand addition concepts (page viii). It is helpful if children can count by twos.

Additional Experiences

Start by showing the children a photograph or drawing of a spider in which the legs are clearly visible. Have children count the number of legs on each side (4) and ask them how many legs a spider has in all (8). Write the addition fact 4 + 4 = 8 and emphasize that the spider has the same number of legs on each side. Then have children use balls of clay and pipe cleaner pieces to make their own creatures. The only rule is that their creature must have the same number of legs on each side. Children should write an addition fact for each creature they make.

Additional practice can be found in *Fact Practice Workbooks, Levels 1-5,* by Creative Publications, Inc.

Doubles Strategy

Warm-Ups

Each warm-up problem set should take two (2) or three (3) minutes. The short problem sets are great for filling transition times. Some teachers use them while children stand in line.

Materials

▶ Number cards 1–10

Talk About It

As you work through these warm-ups, ask children to talk about their thinking. This not only helps you assess, but gives children a chance to clarify their thinking and to hear about ways of thinking that might be different from theirs. You might ask questions like

What kind of number is a double?
(An even number.)

What are some addition facts that are doubles? (1 + 1, 2 + 2, . . .)

A great question to keep the discussion going is

Does anyone have a different answer?

Day 1

Count by ones to 10.
(1, 2, 3, 4, 5, 6, 7, 8, 9, 10)

Count by twos to 20.
(2, 4, 6, 8, 10, 12, 14, 16, 18, 20)

Extension Have children count by twos to 40.

Day 2

Hold up a number card, such as 5.

Show this number of fingers on one hand. How many fingers are you showing?
(5)

Show this number of fingers on each hand. How many fingers are you showing altogether?
(10)

Repeat this activity using number cards of 5 or less.

Extension Ask children

How could you show doubles for the numbers 6 through 10?
(Flash fingers twice or work with a partner.)

Day 3

Hold up a number card, such as 10.

Draw a row with this number of dots. How many dots?
(10)

Draw another dot below each dot in the row. How many dots altogether?
(20)

Extension Repeat this activity holding up number cards with numbers 11 through 20.

Day 4

Hold up a number card, such as 5.

Write this number. Count on two and write the numbers as you count.
(5, 6, 7)

Show children a card with the double of the number card just shown.
(10)

Write this number below the first number you wrote. Count on two numbers, counting by twos, and write the numbers as you count.
(10, 12, 14)

Say the numbers in each row.
(5, 6, 7, followed by 10, 12, 14)

Extension Repeat this activity holding up number cards with numbers 6 through 10.

Day 5

Hold up a number card, such as 3.

Write this number. Count on three and write the numbers as you count.
(3, 4, 5, 6)

Show children a card with the double of the number card just shown.
(6)

Write this number below the first number you wrote. Count on three numbers, counting by twos, and write the numbers as you count.
(6, 8, 10, 12)

Say the numbers in each row.
(3, 4, 5, 6, followed by 6, 8, 10, 12)

Extension Repeat this activity holding up number cards with numbers from 6 through 10.

Double Time

Summary

Children create posters to illustrate doubles facts. They will use these mental images as they memorize their doubles facts.

Materials

▶ Posterboard and art material needed to make posters

Directions

❶ Explain to children that doubles facts are a special group of facts. For doubles facts, both addends are the same.

❷ Ask children if they can think of some things that come in pairs. (Answers might include eyes in your head, wheels on a bicycle, arms or legs on a person's body, wings on a bird, or twins.)

Hold up your hands and say

What about our fingers? Five plus five equals . . . (10).

❸ Have children create a poster of the doubles facts from 1 + 1 to 10 + 10 showing all ten facts and at least one illustration of each. Examples of doubles can be found all around.

notes Here are some ideas for illustrating doubles facts. Your students will think of many more.

1 + 1	human legs, human arms, eyes, ears, twins
2 + 2	dog legs (and other animal legs), chair legs
3 + 3	insect legs, pair of tricycles
4 + 4	spider legs, two chairs' legs
5 + 5	fingers on two hands, toes on two feet, points of two stars
6 + 6	rows of eggs in a dozen egg carton
7 + 7	two flowers with seven petals each
8 + 8	two spiders' legs
9 + 9	two minivans with 9 people each
10 + 10	number of fingers, number of toes, two peoples' worth of fingers or toes

Extension

Make one copy of pages 32 and 33 for each group of children that will play. Each group will also need one game marker per child plus a blank spinner for the group. Students use the spinner on page 32 and move their markers along the game path on page 33.

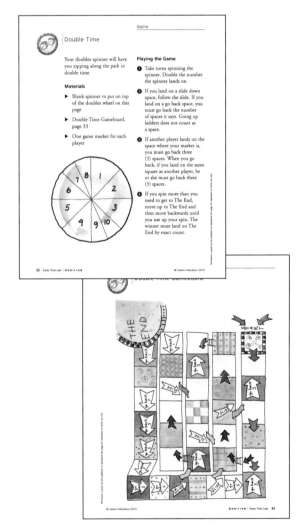

Double Time

Your doubles spinner will have you zipping along the path in double time.

Materials

▶ Blank spinner to put on top of the doubles wheel on this page

▶ Double Time Gameboard, page 33

▶ One game marker for each player

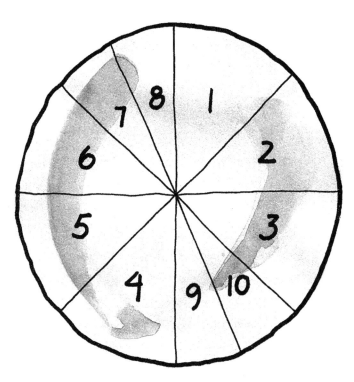

Playing the Game

❶ Take turns spinning the spinner. Double the number the spinner lands on.

❷ If you land on a slide-down space, follow the slide. If you land on a go-back space, you must go back the number of spaces it says. Going up ladders does not count as a space.

❸ If another player lands on the space where your marker is, you must go back three (3) spaces. When you go back, if you land on the same square as another player, he or she must go back three (3) spaces.

❹ If you spin more than you need to get to The End, move up to The End and then move backwards until you use up your spin. The winner must land on The End by exact count.

Double Time Gameboard

Doubles Strategy

Practice

Work on these sets of practice exercises until children get each answer within three (3) seconds. Ask children to state the entire fact rather than just the answer ("4 + 4 = 8," instead of "8"). Stating the complete fact improves students' recall. Present the facts in various ways. Ask the children to listen and then reply verbally, or use flash cards and have the children write their facts. Varying the format helps all children focus on the facts.

Talk About It

Ask children to tell you about their thinking. Follow up by asking if anyone thinks about finding the answers a different way.

Can a double be an odd number?
(No.)

How do you find the double of a number?
(Accept all valid methods.)

Day 1

Present these facts.

4 + 4 (8)

7 + 7 (14)

2 + 2 (4)

5 + 5 (10)

0 + 0 (0)

3 + 3 (6)

9 + 9 (18)

1 + 1 (2)

10 + 10 (20)

6 + 6 (12)

8 + 8 (16)

Extension Ask children to give sums for doubles of numbers 11 through 20.

Day 2

Show children a number card, such as 3.

Write the doubles fact and the sum.

$(3 + 3 = 6)$

Continue this activity using all of the number cards 0 through 10.

Extension Repeat this activity using number cards 11 through 20.

Day 3

Present these facts.

10 + 10 (20)

3 + 3 (6)

6 + 6 (12)

2 + 2 (4)

5 + 5 (10)

7 + 7 (14)

4 + 4 (8)

0 + 0 (0)

8 + 8 (16)

1 + 1 (2)

9 + 9 (18)

Extension Ask children to give sums for doubles of numbers 11 through 20.

Day 4

Show children a number card of an even number from 0 through 20, such as 4.

Write the doubles fact that has this number as the result.

$(2 + 2 = 4)$

Repeat this procedure until all of the number cards have been used.

Extension Use the even numbers from 22–40.

Day 5

Present these facts.

1 + 1 (2)

8 + 8 (16)

5 + 5 (10)

9 + 9 (18)

4 + 4 (8)

10 + 10 (20)

0 + 0 (0)

7 + 7 (14)

3 + 3 (6)

6 + 6 (12)

2 + 2 (4)

Extension Ask children to give sums for doubles of numbers 11 through 20.

Near-Doubles Strategy Overview

What is the Near-Doubles Strategy?

The near-doubles strategy is a combination of counting on and doubles. When addends are only one or two numbers apart, double the lesser number and then count on one or two. For example, to add 8 + 6, think (double 6) + 2, or 12, 13, 14. Conversely, double the greater number and count back. With this method, to add 8 + 6, think (double 8) −2, or 16, 15, 14.

When to Use the Near Doubles Strategy

The near-doubles strategy applies to addition facts in which the addends differ by one or two.

+	0	1	2	3	4	5	6	7	8	9	10
0		1	2								
1	1		3	4							
2	2	3		5	6						
3		4	5		7	8					
4			6	7		9	10				
5				8	9		11	12			
6					10	11		13	14		
7						12	13		15	16	
8							14	15		17	18
9								16	17		19
10									18	19	

Prerequisites

Children should understand addition concepts (page viii). They should also be adept with the count-on and doubles strategies.

Additional Experiences

Use LinkerCubes® to model near-doubles facts. Have children place towers of linked cubes representing addends next to each other. Then, have them write the addition fact represented by the towers. Remind children of the related doubles fact and ask how they can use that doubles fact to remember the fact for their towers. Some children may observe that when the addends differ by two, their sum is equal to the doubles fact for the counting number that falls between the two addends. For example, 6 + 8 is the same as 7 + 7.

Additional practice can be found in *Fact Practice Workbooks,* Levels 1-5, by Creative Publications, Inc.

3 + 4 = 7

Near-Doubles Strategy

Warm-Ups

Each warm-up exercise set should take two (2) or three (3) minutes. The short exercise sets are great for filling transition times. Some teachers use them while children stand in line.

Materials

▶ Number cards from 0–10 and multiples of 5 through 50

Talk About It

As you work through these warm-ups, ask children to talk about their thinking. This not only helps you assess, but gives children a chance to clarify their thinking and to hear about ways of thinking that might be different from theirs. You might ask questions like

How might you use the double 2 + 2 to find the sum of 2 + 3?
(Since 2 + 2 = 4, and 2 + 3 is one more, 2 + 3 = 5.)

How might you use the double 4 + 4 to find the sum of 3 + 4?
(Since 4 + 4 = 8, and 3 + 4 is one less, 3 + 4 = 7.)

We call 2 + 3 and 3 + 4 near doubles. How are doubles and near doubles related?
(Doubles have two addends that are the same. Near doubles have addends that are very close to each other.)

A great question to keep the discussion going is

Does anyone have a different way to explain near doubles?

Day 1

Show children a number card, such as 2.

Double this number.
(4)

Count on one. What is the result?
(5)

Repeat this activity using number cards 0 through 5.

Extension Repeat this activity using multiples of 10, up to 50.

Day 2

Show children a number card, such as 8.

What is the double of this number?
(16)

Repeat this activity using number cards 6 through 10.

Extension Repeat this activity using multiples of 10, up to 50.

Day 3

Show children a number card, such as 7.

Double this number.
(14)

Count on one. What is the result?
(15)

Repeat this activity using number cards 0 through 10.

Extension Repeat this activity using multiples of 10, up to 50.

Day 4

Show children a number card, such as 9.

Double this number.
(18)

Count on (one or two). What is the result?
(19 or 20)

Repeat this activity using number cards 0 through 10.

Extension Repeat this activity using multiples of 5, up to 50.

Day 5

Show children a number card, such as 6.

Double this number.

(12)

Count on two. What is the result?

(14)

Repeat this activity using number cards 0 through 5.

Extension Repeat this activity using multiples of 10, up to 50.

Day 6

Show children a number card, such as 10.

Double this number.

(20)

Count on two. What is the result?

(22)

Repeat this activity using number cards 6 through 10.

Extension Repeat this activity using multiples of 10, up to 50.

Day 7

Show children a number card, such as 3.

Double this number.

(6)

Count on two. What is the result?

(8)

Repeat this activity using number cards 0 through 10.

Extension Repeat this activity using multiples of 5, up to 50.

Day 8

Show children a number card, such as 4.

Double this number.

(8)

Count on (one or two). What is the result?

(9 or 10)

Repeat this activity using number cards 0 through 10.

Extension Repeat this activity using multiples of 5, up to 50.

Day 9

Show children a number card, such as 7.

Double this number.

(14)

Count on (zero, one, or two). What is the result?

(14, 15, or 16)

Repeat this activity using number cards 0 through 10.

Extension Repeat this activity using multiples of 10, up to 50.

Day 10

Show children a number card, such as 0.

Double this number.

(0)

Count on (zero, one, or two). What is the result?

(0, 1, or 2)

Repeat this activity using number cards 0 through 10.

Extension Repeat this activity using multiples of 5, up to 50.

Seeing Double

Summary

Children use LinkerCubes® and GeoMirrors to create near doubles exercises.

●●●
Small Group Activity

Materials

Each pair of children needs

▶ A GeoMirror

▶ Twenty (20) LinkerCubes®

▶ A copy of Seeing Double GeoMirror Puzzle, page 44

> **notes** If GeoMirrors are not available, have children build trains with LinkerCubes and place them on a sheet of paper that has a dividing line drawn down the center. Children should build trains of equal length and place one on either side of the line. Additional cubes can then be added to one side.

Directions

❶ Give each pair of students a GeoMirror, LinkerCubes®, and a copy of GeoMirror Puzzle (page 44). Work through the example at the top of page 44 with the children.

❷ Have children display each sum listed on the worksheet following these steps. First, place cubes in front of the GeoMirror. Next, add together the actual cubes and those reflected in the GeoMirror. Then, add one or two additional cubes behind the GeoMirror in a position that does not overlap with the reflected cubes.

❸ Direct children to record information for each sum they display.

Talk About It

Ask children questions about the GeoMirror Puzzle.

What types of numbers have one counter behind the GeoMirror?
(Odd numbers)

What types of numbers have two counters behind the GeoMirror?
(Even numbers)

Using the numbers you wrote, can you make up a rule that tells how to find the sum?
(Double the number of counters in front of the GeoMirror, then add the number of counters behind it. Or, the number of counters in front plus the number reflected, added to the number behind.)

Think about the GeoMirror patterns and addition facts. Suppose we use the rule that an addition fact begins with the number telling how many cubes are placed in front of the GeoMirror. Then, we add a second number. How would we state the fact that has a first addend of 2, and a sum of 6?

You may want to have students set up the problem with cubes. The fact would be 2 + 4 = 6. Have the class try a few more.

Write several of the near doubles facts on the board. Ask children to tell you the sum of each fact and how they figured it out. When a child tells about the near-doubles strategy, ask other questions to tie that thinking to the GeoMirror activity.

Extensions

Have children use page 45 to first draw, then write, their own near-doubles exercises. Introduce the page by reminding children of the rule they followed to write facts earlier. Each addition written should have two addends and should start with the number that tells how many cubes are placed in front of the GeoMirror. The second addend should complete the fact to produce the sum.

> It is interesting to examine the near-doubles diagonals on the addition chart. You may want to make a copy of page 86 for each child in your class, have students identify all of the facts where the addends differ by one, and then, look for patterns. They could then do the same thing for facts where the addends differ by two.

Seeing Double GeoMirror Puzzle

❶ Put 4 counters in front of the GeoMirror.

❷ Put 2 counters behind the GeoMirror.

❸ How many counters do you see in all?

_____ counters

❹ Put some counters in front of the GeoMirror. Put exactly 1 or 2 counters behind the GeoMirror.

❺ How many of the sums below can you see?

Sum	Number in Front	Number Behind
6		
7		
8		
9		
10		
11		
12		
13		
14		
15		
16		
17		
18		

Seeing Double GeoMirror Facts

1.

_____ + _____ = _____

2.

_____ + _____ = _____

3.

_____ + _____ = _____

4.

_____ + _____ = _____

5.

_____ + _____ = _____

6.

_____ + _____ = _____

7.

_____ + _____ = _____

8.

_____ + _____ = _____

9.

_____ + _____ = _____

10.

_____ + _____ = _____

Near-Doubles Strategy

Practice

Work on these sets of practice exercises until children can get each answer within three (3) seconds. Ask children to tell the entire fact rather than just the answer ("4 + 5 = 9," instead of "9"). When children tell the complete fact, it improves their recall. Try presenting the facts in various ways. Ask the children to listen and then reply verbally, or use flash cards and have the children write their facts. Varying the format helps all children focus on the facts.

Talk About It

Ask children to tell you about their thinking. Follow up by asking if anyone has a different way to find the answer.

How can you use doubles to help find near-double facts?

(Double the smaller number and count on the difference between the two addends. Or, double the larger number and count back the difference between the two addends.)

Can you give an addition fact for which you could use the near-doubles strategy? Tell what you would do.

(Accept all valid responses.)

Day 1

Have children calculate these sums.

3 + 4 (7)	3 + 3 + 1 (7)
1 + 2 (3)	1 + 1 + 1 (3)
4 + 4 (8)	4 + 4 + 0 (8)
3 + 3 (6)	3 + 3 + 0 (6)
2 + 3 (5)	2 + 2 + 1 (5)
5 + 5 (10)	5 + 5 + 0 (10)
4 + 5 (9)	4 + 4 + 1 (9)
1 + 1 (2)	1 + 1 + 0 (2)
0 + 1 (1)	0 + 0 + 1 (1)
2 + 2 (4)	2 + 2 + 0 (4)
5 + 6 (11)	5 + 5 + 1 (11)
0 + 0 (0)	0 + 0 + 0 (0)

Extension Have children calculate sums using multiples of 10, through 50. (Example: 20 + 21 = 20 + 20 + 1.)

Day 2

Have children calculate these sums.

8 + 9 (17)	8 + 8 + 1 (17)
6 + 7 (13)	6 + 6 + 1 (13)
9 + 9 (18)	9 + 9 + 0 (18)
8 + 8 (16)	8 + 8 + 0 (16)
10 + 11 (21)	10 + 10 + 1 (21)
7 + 7 (14)	7 + 7 + 0 (14)
9 + 10 (19)	9 + 9 + 1 (19)
6 + 6 (12)	6 + 6 + 0 (12)
7 + 8 (15)	7 + 7 + 1 (15)
10 + 10 (20)	10 + 10 + 0 (20)

Extension Have children calculate sums using multiples of 5, through 50. (Example: 25 + 26 = 25 + 25 + 1.)

Day 3

Present these facts.

4 + 5 (9)	7 + 8 (15)
1 + 1 (2)	5 + 5 (10)
8 + 8 (16)	8 + 9 (17)
5 + 6 (11)	3 + 4 (7)
0 + 1 (1)	10 + 10 (20)
3 + 3 (6)	1 + 2 (3)
9 + 10 (19)	4 + 4 (8)
2 + 2 (4)	9 + 9 (18)
10 + 11 (21)	7 + 7 (14)
6 + 6 (12)	2 + 3 (5)

Extension Have children calculate sums using multiples of 5, through 50. Present the double or the double plus 1.

Day 4

Present these facts.

4 + 3 (7)	7 + 6 (13)
5 + 5 (10)	8 + 7 (15)
7 + 8 (15)	1 + 1 (2)
6 + 5 (11)	9 + 10 (19)
8 + 8 (16)	3 + 2 (5)
1 + 2 (3)	10 + 10 (20)
3 + 3 (6)	3 + 4 (7)
9 + 8 (17)	6 + 7 (13)
4 + 5 (9)	2 + 3 (5)
6 + 6 (12)	1 + 0 (1)

Extension Have children calculate sums using multiples of 5, through 50. Present the double or the double plus 1.

Day 5

Have children calculate these sums.

3 + 5 (8)	3 + 3 + 2 (8)
4 + 4 (8)	4 + 4 + 0 (8)
2 + 4 (6)	2 + 2 + 2 (6)
1 + 3 (4)	1 + 1 + 2 (4)
0 + 2 (2)	0 + 0 + 2 (2)
3 + 3 (6)	3 + 3 + 0 (6)
0 + 0 (0)	0 + 0 + 0 (0)
4 + 6 (10)	4 + 4 + 2 (10)
2 + 2 (4)	2 + 2 + 0 (4)
5 + 5 (10)	5 + 5 + 0 (10)
1 + 1 (2)	1 + 1 + 0 (2)
5 + 7 (12)	5 + 5 + 2 (12)

Extension Have children calculate sums using multiples of 10, through 50. (Example: 20 + 22, 20 + 20 + 2.)

Day 6

Have children calculate these sums.

6 + 8 (14)	6 + 6 + 2 (14)
7 + 7 (14)	7 + 7 + 0 (14)
8 + 10 (18)	8 + 8 + 2 (18)
6 + 6 (12)	6 + 6 + 0 (12)
7 + 9 (16)	7 + 7 + 2 (16)
9 + 9 (18)	9 + 9 + 0 (18)
8 + 8 (16)	8 + 8 + 0 (16)
10 + 12 (22)	10 + 10 + 2 (21)
9 + 11 (20)	9 + 9 + 2 (20)
10 + 10 (20)	10 + 10 + 0 (20)

Extension Have children calculate sums using multiples of 5, through 50.

Day 7

Present these facts.

4 + 6 (10)	2 + 2 (4)
3 + 3 (6)	6 + 8 (14)
9 + 11 (20)	6 + 6 (12)
5 + 5 (10)	5 + 7 (12)
4 + 4 (8)	8 + 10 (18)
7 + 9 (16)	3 + 5 (8)
0 + 2 (2)	10 + 10 (20)
9 + 9 (18)	1 + 1 (2)
2 + 4 (6)	1 + 3 (4)
8 + 8 (16)	7 + 7 (14)

Extension Have children calculate sums using multiples of 5, through 50. Present the double or the double plus 2.

Day 8

Present these facts.

4 + 2 (6)	7 + 5 (12)
5 + 5 (10)	0 + 2 (2)
7 + 9 (16)	3 + 1 (4)
6 + 4 (10)	9 + 7 (16)
8 + 6 (14)	3 + 3 (6)
1 + 3 (4)	10 + 10 (20)
0 + 0 (0)	4 + 6 (10)
10 + 8 (18)	6 + 8 (14)
3 + 5 (8)	2 + 2 (4)
6 + 6 (12)	2 + 0 (2)

Extension Have children calculate sums using multiples of 5, through 50. Present the double or the double plus 2.

Day 9

Present these facts.

4 + 5 (9)	7 + 5 (12)
3 + 1 (4)	0 + 2 (2)
7 + 7 (14)	4 + 4 (8)
6 + 8 (14)	7 + 9 (16)
4 + 3 (7)	8 + 7 (15)
5 + 3 (8)	9 + 9 (18)
8 + 8 (16)	4 + 6 (10)
10 + 9 (19)	6 + 5 (11)
3 + 2 (5)	2 + 4 (6)
6 + 7 (13)	5 + 5 (10)

Extension Have children calculate the sums using multiples of 5, through 50. Present the double or the double plus 1 or 2.

Day 10

Present these facts.

2 + 1 (3)	7 + 5 (12)
6 + 4 (10)	2 + 0 (2)
9 + 7 (16)	4 + 4 (8)
2 + 2 (4)	8 + 9 (17)
5 + 3 (8)	9 + 7 (16)
8 + 6 (14)	7 + 7 (14)
5 + 4 (9)	5 + 6 (11)
10 + 9 (19)	4 + 2 (6)
7 + 6 (13)	4 + 3 (7)
9 + 8 (17)	10 + 8 (18)

Extension Have children calculate sums using multiples of 5, through 50. Present the double or the double plus 1 or 2.

Sums-of-Ten Strategy Overview

What is the Sums-of-Ten Strategy?

The sums-of-ten strategy is used with a set of addition facts that will become a cornerstone of powerful number sense for your students. These facts are very helpful in adding numbers with sums greater than ten. Knowledge of this set of facts is a prerequisite to the making-ten strategy.

For some children it is helpful to visualize ten fingers or a ten-frame to remember this set of facts. For other children using double five as a reference point is beneficial. For example, they might think 7 + ? = 10. 7 is 2 + 5, so only 3 more are needed to get the next five. 7 + 3 = 10.

When to Use the Sums of-Ten Strategy

These facts all have sums of ten.

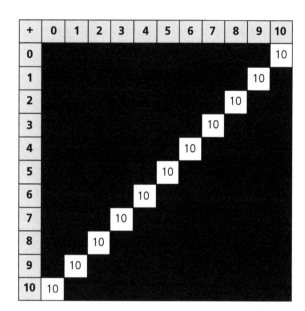

+	0	1	2	3	4	5	6	7	8	9	10
0											10
1										10	
2									10		
3								10			
4							10				
5						10					
6					10						
7				10							
8			10								
9		10									
10	10										

Prerequisite

Children should understand addition concepts (page viii).

Additional Experiences

Present this problem:

Yolanda is using candles to decorate a cake for Brandon's tenth birthday. The candles come in two colors. What are the different ways she can decorate the cake?

Give each child a lump of clay and twenty candles, ten each of two different colors. Ask children make clay "cakes" and to put ten (10) candles on their "cakes." They should record each way of decorating found with an addition fact. When children have found as many facts as they can, discuss their solutions.

Ask questions like

Can you tell me one fact that you found?
(Accept all valid responses.)

Did anyone find a different fact?
(Accept all valid responses.)

Have we named all the possible ways to decorate? How do you know?

(All ten possible combinations are listed on the board. Or, the numbers 0 through 10 all appear as the addend.)

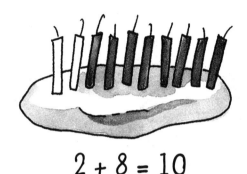

$$2 + 8 = 10$$

Additional practice can be found in *Fact Practice Workbooks,* Levels 1-5, by Creative Publications, Inc.

Sums-of-Ten Strategy

Warm-Ups

Each warm-up problem set should take two (2) or three (3) minutes. The short problem sets are great for filling transition times. Some teachers use them while children stand in line.

Materials

▶ Number cards 0–20

▶ 30 flash cards, including all sums of 10, 10 sums over 10, and 10 sums less than 10

Talk About It

As you work through these warm-ups, ask children to talk about their thinking. This not only helps you assess, but gives children a chance to clarify their thinking and to hear about ways of thinking that might be different from theirs. You might ask questions like

What strategies are helpful in knowing the facts that have a sum of 10?
(Count on, commutative property, doubles, and near doubles.)

How do you know the missing number to make 10?
(Accept all valid responses.)

A great question to keep the discussion going is

Does anyone have a different way to find the answer?

Day 1

Show children a number card from 7 through 10, such as 7.

Count on 3.
(10)

Show another card, such as 10.

Count on 0.
(10)

Repeat this activity using only number cards 7 through 10. Select the number to count on so the result is 10.

Extension Repeat this activity using number cards from 17 through 20. Have children count on to make 20.

Day 2

Present these facts.

4 + 6 (10)

5 + 5 (10)

3 + 7 (10)

6 + 4 (10)

7 + 3 (10)

Repeat facts as many times as you feel appropriate.

Extension Ask children to explain how they find their answers. (Accept all valid responses.)

Day 3

Present these facts.

7 + 3 (10)

4 + 6 (10)

9 + 1 (10)

2 + 8 (10)

10 + 0 (10)

5 + 5 (10)

6 + 4 (10)

1 + 9 (10)

3 + 7 (10)

8 + 2 (10)

0 + 10 (10)

Extension Present facts that have a sum of 20.

Day 4

Present these facts.

8 + 2 (10)

1 + 9 (10)

4 + 6 (10)

10 + 0 (10)

7 + 3 (10)

0 + 10 (10)

2 + 8 (10)

5 + 5 (10)

6 + 4 (10)

9 + 1 (10)

3 + 7 (10)

Extension Present facts that have a sum of 20.

Day 5

Show children a number card, such as 4.

Show this number of fingers on your hand(s).

How many fingers are not showing?
(6)

Continue this activity using number cards 0 through 10.

Extension Show a number card from 10 through 20. Have children work in pairs.

Day 6

Show children a number card, such as 7.

How many more to make 10?
(3)

Continue this activity using number cards 5 through 10.

Extension Show number cards from 15 through 20. How many more to make 20?

Day 7

Show children a number card, such as 5.

How many more to make 10?
(5)

Continue this activity using number cards 0 through 5.

Extension Show number cards from 10 through 15. How many more to make 20?

Day 8

Show children a number card, such as 0.

How many more to make 10?

(10)

Continue this activity using number cards 0 through 10.

Extension Show number cards from 10 through 20. How many more to make 20?

Day 9

Present these facts.

6 + 4 (10)

0 + 10 (10)

3 + 7 (10)

1 + 9 (10)

10 + 0 (10)

5 + 5 (10)

8 + 2 (10)

9 + 1 (10)

7 + 3 (10)

4 + 6 (10)

2 + 8 (10)

Extension Present facts that have a sum of 20.

Day 10

Show children a number card, such as 8.

How many more to make 10?

(2)

Continue this activity using number cards 0 through 10.

Extension Show number cards 10 through 20. How many more to make 20?

Full Frame

Summary

Children use a ten-frame and cubes to build facts with sums of ten. They write the facts that describe the full frames.

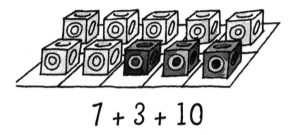

$$7 + 3 + 10$$

Materials

Each child needs

▶ A copy of Full Frame, page 58

▶ Two copies Full Frame Recording Sheet, page 59

▶ Twenty (20) LinkerCubes®, ten (10) each of two colors

Directions

❶ Show children how to place LinkerCubes® into the ten-frame printed on page 58. Have children start at the top left corner of the ten-frame and fill across. Place the sixth cube in the lower left corner of the frame, then continue filling across the row. When filled, the ten-frames for 7 and 3 should always look like the frames shown below.

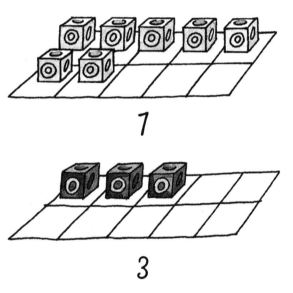

7

3

❷ Instruct children to place all of the cubes of one color before switching to the second color. That way the colors will represent just two addends. If children switch back and forth between the colors, they'll be building a number sentence with more than two addends.

❸ Ask children to write an addition fact to represent the cubes placed in the ten-frame.

4 Children should follow the directions, placing cubes into the ten-frame provided in Full Frame, page 58. Their facts for sums of ten should be recorded on the Full Frame Recording Sheet, page 59. When completed, all eleven facts should be recorded on page 59.

Talk About It

When children have found all the combinations of ten, ask questions like

What is one fact with a sum of ten?
(Any of 0 + 10, 1 + 9, 2 + 8, 3 + 7, 4 + 6, 5 + 5, 6 + 4, 7 + 3, 8 + 2, 9 + 1, 10 + 0.)

Does anyone have a different fact with a sum of ten?
(Accept all accurate responses.)

Are there any more facts with a sum of ten?
When you have recorded all eleven addition facts that have sums of ten and the answer is "no," ask

How do you know?
(Because there are only eleven (11) addition facts that have sums of ten. Or, because they used zero (0) first, then 1, then 2, on up through 10 and they know from the pattern that they have all the facts. Accept all reasonable answers.)

Does anyone have a way that helps him or her remember addition facts that add up to ten?
(There are many possible answers here. Some children might "just know," others will think about how the ten-frame looks, some might think about ten fingers, and yet others will have a variety of ideas that work for them. Accept all reasonable answers.)

Extension

Invite children to play "Race to 100." In this game, players are provided a bag containing the numbers zero (0) through ten (10). Players take turns pulling a number from the bag, then telling what number should be added to the one pulled to make a sum of ten. That second number is then recorded on the child's paper. For example, if 3 is pulled, 7 would be recorded on the paper. The recorded numbers are added together and the first child to reach or pass a sum of one hundred (100) wins.

Full Frame

Fill the ten-frame with two colors of LinkerCubes® to show a fact that has a sum of ten. Can you find all the ways to make ten with just two addends?

Directions

1 Use LinkerCubes® to fill up the ten-frame.

2 Use a small ten-frame on your Full Frame Recording Sheet, page 59, to show how the filled ten-frame looks.

3 Write the addition fact in the spaces under the small ten-frame.

4 Find as many different facts as you can.

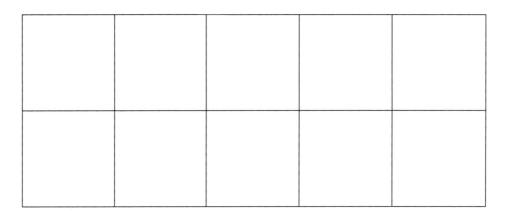

Full Frame Recording Sheet

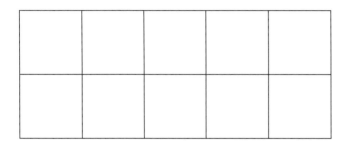

___ + ___ = 10

___ + ___ = 10

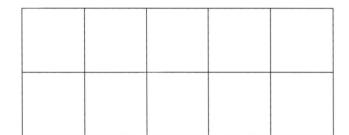
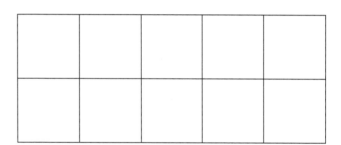

___ + ___ = 10

___ + ___ = 10

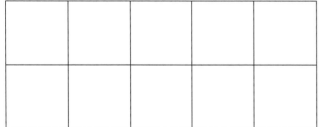

___ + ___ = 10

___ + ___ = 10

Sums-of-Ten Strategy

Practice

Work on these sets of practice exercises until children can get each answer within three (3) seconds. Ask children to tell the entire fact rather than just the answer ("3 + 7 = 10," instead of "10"). When children tell the complete fact, it improves their recall. Try presenting the facts in various ways. Ask the children to listen and then reply verbally, or use flash cards and have the children write their facts. Varying the format helps all children focus on the facts.

Talk About It

Ask children to talk about their thinking. Follow up by asking if anyone has a different way to find the answer.

How do you know if a sum is less than 10 or greater than 10?
(Accept all valid responses.)

How do you know how much less or how much greater?
(Accept all valid responses.)

How can knowing sums of 10 be of help in learning other addition facts?
(Sums for facts with addends close to sums of ten can be found in a similar way to finding near doubles.)

Day 1

Choose flash cards that have a sum of 10. Show one flash card to the children, such as 3 + 7.

What is the sum?
(10)

Continue showing flash cards until all have been shown at least once.

Extension Verbally present facts that have a sum of 20.

Day 2
Show children a number card, such as 6.

How many more to make 10?
(4)

Continue activity showing number cards 5 through 10.

Extension Repeat activity using number cards from 15 through 20.

How many more to make 20?

Day 3
Show children a number card, such as 3.

How many more to make 10?
(7)

Continue activity showing number cards 0 through 10.

Extension Repeat activity using number cards from 10 through 15.

How many more to make 20?

Day 4
Show children a number card, such as 7.

How many more to make 10?
(3)

Continue activity using number cards 0 through 10.

Extension Repeat activity using number cards from 10 through 20.

How many more to make 20?

Day 5

Show children a number card, such as 5.

How many more to make 10?
(5)

Continue activity using number cards 0 through 10.

Extension Repeat activity using number cards from 10 through 20.

How many more to make 20?

Day 6

Show children one flash card, such as 6 + 3.

Is the sum 10 or less than 10?
(Less than 10)

Continue this activity using flash cards with sums of 10 and sums less than ten.

Extension Repeat this activity adding the question

How much less?

Day 7

Show children one flash card, such as 8 + 6.

Is the sum 10 or greater than 10?
(Greater than 10)

Continue this activity using flash cards with sums of ten and sums greater than ten.

Extension Repeat this activity adding the question

How much greater?

Day 8

Choose ten (10) addition flash cards so that some have a sum of 10, a sum less than 10, and a sum greater than 10.

Show children one flash card, such as 5 + 7.

Is the sum 10, less than 10, or greater than 10? (Greater than 10)

Continue this activity until all cards have been shown at least once.

Extension Repeat this activity adding the question

How much less? or ***How much greater?***

Day 9

Show children a number card, such as 9.

How many more to make 10? (1)

Continue this activity using number cards 0 through 10.

Extension Repeat this activity using number cards 10 through 20.

How many more to make 20?

Day 10

Choose ten (10) addition flash cards so that some have a sum of 10, a sum less than 10, and a sum greater than 10.

Show children one flash card, such as 9 + 7.

Is the sum 10, less than 10, or greater than 10? (Greater than 10)

Continue this activity until all cards have been shown at least once.

Extension Repeat this activity adding the question

How much less? or ***How much greater?***

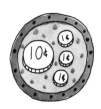

Adding-Ten Strategy Overview

What is the Adding-Ten Strategy?

The adding-ten strategy is one that almost all children naturally use and quickly grasp. You simply add one ten to the tens place.

When to Use the Adding-Ten Strategy

The adding-ten strategy is used when one of the addends is ten.

+	0	1	2	3	4	5	6	7	8	9	10
0											10
1											11
2											12
3											13
4											14
5											15
6											16
7											17
8											18
9											19
10	10	11	12	13	14	15	16	17	18	19	

Prerequisites

Children should understand addition concepts (page viii). They should also have experience with adding zero. It is helpful if they have some groundwork in place value, particularly the idea of tens and ones.

Additional Experiences

Give the children 0–99 charts and explore what happens when you go down one row.

0	1	2	3	4	5	6	7	8	9
10	11	12	13	14	15	16	17	18	19
20	21	22	23	24	25	26	27	28	29
30	31	32	33	34	35	36	37	38	39
40	41	42	43	44	45	46	47	48	49
50	51	52	53	54	55	56	57	58	59
60	61	62	63	64	65	66	67	68	69
70	71	72	73	74	75	76	77	78	79
80	81	82	83	84	85	86	87	88	89
90	91	92	93	94	95	96	97	98	99

Place a finger on 7. Move your finger down one row. What number is your finger on now?

(17)

In moving down one row, how much have we added to seven?

(10)

Try other examples. Then ask

Is ten always added to the number when we go down one row?

(Yes.)

Do you see any patterns that will help you add ten without a chart?

(You just add one ten to the tens place.)

Concentrate on moving between the first and second row, but you will see that most children very quickly generalize the plus-ten rule to all the rows in the chart.

Additional practice can be found in *Fact Practice Workbooks,* Levels 1-5, by Creative Publications, Inc.

Adding-Ten Strategy

Warm-Ups

Each warm-up exercise set should take 2 or 3 minutes. The short exercise sets are great for filling transition times. Some teachers use them while children stand in line.

Materials

▶ Number cards 0–19

Talk About It

As you work through these warm-ups, ask children to talk about their thinking. This not only helps you assess, but gives children a chance to clarify their thinking and to hear about ways of thinking that might be different from theirs. You might ask questions like

What is the result when you add 0 to a number?
(The number stays the same.)

With a one-digit number, what is the place value of the number?
(Ones.)

With a two-digit number, what is the place value of the numeral at the left?
(Tens.)

What is the place value of the numeral at the right?
(Ones.)

Day 1

Show a number card, such as 7.

Add 0 to this number. What is the result?
(7)

Continue this activity using number cards 0 through 9.

Extension Repeat this activity using number cards from 10 through 19.

Day 2

Show a number card, such as 2.

What is 0 plus this number?
(2)

Continue this activity using number cards 0 through 9.

Extension Repeat this activity using number cards from 10 through 19.

Day 3

Show a number card, such as 15.

What is the numeral in the ones place?
(5)

What is the numeral in the tens place?
(1)

Continue this activity using number cards 10 through 19.

Extension Repeat this activity using numbers cards 20 through 99.

Day 4

Show children a number card, such as 12.

Add 1 one to the ones place. What is the new number?
(13)

Add 1 ten to the tens place. What is the new number?
(23)

Continue this activity using number cards 0 through 19.

Extension Repeat this activity using number cards 20 through 99.

Day 5

Show children a number card, such as 14.

Add 1 one to the ones place. What is the new number?
(15)

Add 1 ten to the tens place. What is the new number:
(25)

Continue this activity using number cards 0 through 19.

Extension Repeat this activity using number cards 20 through 99.

10-Sticks

Summary

Children link ten (10) LinkerCubes® into a 10-stick. They use ten (10) loose cubes with the 10-stick to model adding ten to one-digit numbers.

Materials

Each child needs

▶ A copy of 10-Sticks, page 69

▶ Twenty (20) LinkerCubes®

Directions

❶ Ask children to link ten (10) LinkerCubes® together. Tell them that for this activity they will use this 10-stick for ten.

❷ Have them put two individual LinkerCubes next to the 10-stick and tell what number they have (12).

❸ Ask children to write the fact that tells what they did (10 + 2 = 12).

❹ Request that children not link the separate cubes that remain after they have put together one 10-stick. Tell them that it will be easier to figure out the sums if they link only tens.

❺ Give children a copy of 10-Sticks, page 69. They will first use the LinkerCubes to model the exercises listed, then make up some of their own plus ten activities.

❻ When children finish page 69, bring them together and ask questions. Write all answers on the board.

What fact did you write that used a 10-stick? (Answers will vary.)

Did anyone write a different 10-stick fact? (Answers will vary.)

Did you notice any patterns to the facts? (They all added ten. When you add ten to a one-digit number, with the exception of eleven and twelve, the answer is in the "teens." When you add ten, you just add one ten to the tens place.)

$$10 + 2 = 12$$

10-Sticks

Use your 10-stick and LinkerCubes® to show "plus ten" addition facts.

Directions

❶ Use the 10-stick and cubes listed to make addition facts.

❷ Draw the cubes and sticks.

❸ Write the fact.

On the back of this paper, write your own 10-stick plus cubes descriptions. How many different ones can you find?

One 10-stick plus 2 cubes

_____ + _____ = _____

One 10-stick plus 5 cubes

_____ + _____ = _____

3 cubes plus one 10-stick

_____ + _____ = _____

9 cubes plus one 10-stick

_____ + _____ = _____

one 10-stick plus 6 cubes

_____ + _____ = _____

1 cube plus one 10-stick

_____ + _____ = _____

Adding-Ten Strategy

Practice

Work on these sets of practice until children can get each answer within three (3) seconds. Ask children to tell the entire fact rather than just the answer ("4 + 10 = 14," instead of "14"). When children tell the complete fact, it improves their recall. Try presenting the facts in various ways. Ask the children to listen and then reply verbally, or use flash cards and have the children write their facts. Varying the format helps all children focus on the facts.

Talk About It

Ask children to talk about their thinking. Follow up by asking if anyone has a different way to find the answer.

What happens to the tens digit when 10 is added?

(The numeral in the tens place increases by one.)

What happens to the ones digit when 10 is added?

(The ones digit remains the same.)

Day 1
Present these facts.

10 + 4 (14)	10 + 6 (16)
10 + 7 (17)	10 + 1 (11)
10 + 0 (10)	10 + 9 (19)
10 + 2 (12)	10 + 3 (13)
10 + 8 (18)	10 + 5 (15)

Extension Have children add a one-digit number to any multiple of 10, through 90.

Day 2
Present these facts.

3 + 10 (13)	2 + 10 (12)
0 + 10 (10)	5 + 10 (15)
6 + 10 (16)	9 + 10 (19)
1 + 10 (11)	7 + 10 (17)
8 + 10 (18)	4 + 10 (14)

Extension Ask children to add any multiple of 10 to a one-digit number.

Day 3

Show children a number card, such as 6.

Add 10 to this number. What is the result?
(16)

Continue this activity using each of the number cards, 0 through 9, at least once.

Extension Repeat the activity asking children to add other multiples of 10 to the number shown.

Day 4

Show children a number card, such as 6.

Add 10 to the number on the card. What is the result?
(16)

Continue this activity using each of the number cards, 0 through 9, at least once.

Extension Repeat the activity asking children to add other multiples of 10 to the number shown.

Day 5

Present these facts.

6 + 10 (16)	10 + 3 (13)
10 + 4 (14)	7 + 10 (17)
3 + 10 (13)	2 + 10 (12)
8 + 10 (18)	10 + 0 (10)
10 + 1 (11)	1 + 10 (11)
0 + 10 (10)	5 + 10 (15)
10 + 7 (17)	10 + 2 (12)
10 + 5 (15)	10 + 8 (18)
4 + 10 (14)	9 + 10 (19)
10 + 9 (19)	10 + 6 (16)

Extension Repeat the activity using number cards 0 through 9. Ask children to add any multiple of 10 to the number shown.

Making-Ten Strategy Overview

What is the Making-Ten Strategy?

With the making-ten strategy, children deconstruct one of the addends in order to get a number that can be combined with the other addend to make ten. The leftovers are then added to ten to get the sum. For example, for 8 + 4 children could think $8 + 4 = 8 + (2 + 2) = (8 + 2) + 2 = 10 + 2 = 12$.

When to Use the Making Ten Strategy?

The making-ten strategy is used when addition facts have addends of less than ten and the sum is greater than ten.

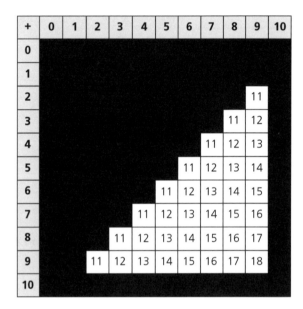

+	0	1	2	3	4	5	6	7	8	9	10
0											
1											
2										11	
3									11	12	
4								11	12	13	
5							11	12	13	14	
6						11	12	13	14	15	
7					11	12	13	14	15	16	
8				11	12	13	14	15	16	17	
9			11	12	13	14	15	16	17	18	
10											

Prerequisites

Children should understand addition concepts (page viii). They should also be adept at using the sums-of-ten and adding-ten strategies.

Additional Experiences

Use pennies and dimes to model addition. You will need two bags; one containing numbers six (6) through nine (9) and the other containing the numbers three (3) through nine (9). Generate exercises by pulling a number from each bag. Place pennies in two groups to represent the two numbers drawn. Move pennies from one group to make enough pennies in the other group to trade for a dime. Write the addends and sums.

Additional practice can be found in *Fact Practice Workbooks,* Levels 1-5, by Creative Publications, Inc.

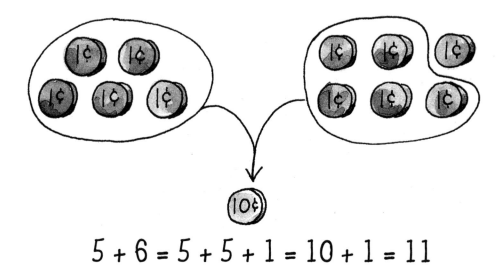

$$5 + 6 = 5 + 5 + 1 = 10 + 1 = 11$$

Making-Ten Strategy

Warm-Ups

Each warm-up problem set should take two (2) or three (3) minutes. The short problem sets are great for filling transition times. Some teachers use them while children stand in line.

Materials

▶ Flash cards with sums of 10 or greater

▶ Number cards 0–9

Talk About It

As you work through these warm-ups, ask children to talk about their thinking. This not only helps you assess, but gives children a chance to clarify their thinking and to hear about ways of thinking that might be different from theirs. You might ask questions like

How do you know how many more you need to make 10?
(Accept all valid responses.)

How do you know how many are left over after you've made 10?
(Accept all valid methods.)

A great question to keep the discussion going is

Does anyone have a different way to find the answer?

Day 1

Show children a number card, such as 2.

Add 10 to this number. What is the result?
(12)

Continue, using number cards 0 through 9, until each card has been shown at least once.

Extension Ask children to add 20 to the number card shown.

Day 2

Show children a number card, such as 8.

What is ten plus this number?
(18)

Continue, using number cards 0 through 9, until each card has been shown at least once.

Extension Ask children to add 20 to the number card shown.

Day 3

Show children a number card, such as 4.

Show this number of fingers on your hand(s).
How many more fingers to make 10?
(6)

Continue, using number cards 0 through 10.

Extension Repeat activity asking

How many more to make 20?

Have children work in pairs.

Day 4

Show children a number card, such as 3.

How many more to make 10?
(7)

Repeat activity using number cards 0 through 10.

Extension Show number cards from 10 through 20.

How many more to make 20?

Day 5

Show children a number card, such as 9.

How many more to make 10?
(1)

Repeat activity using number cards 0 through 10.

Extension Show number cards from 10 through 20.

How many more to make 20?

Day 6

Show children the number card 9.

Add 5 to the number shown.

How many more to make 10? (1)

How many left over? (4)

Repeat this activity. Show number cards 8, 7, 6, and 5 in descending order.

Extension Repeat this activity mixing the order of the number cards.

Day 7

Show children the number card 9.

Add 6 to the number shown.

How many more to make 10? (1)

How many left over? (5)

Repeat this activity. Show number cards 8, 7, 6, 5, and 4 in descending order.

Extension Repeat this activity mixing the order of the number cards.

Day 8

Show children the number card 9.

Add 7 to the number shown.

How many more to make 10? (1)

How many left over? (6)

Repeat this activity. Show number cards 8 through 3 in descending order.

Extension Repeat this activity mixing the order of the number cards.

Day 9

Select pairs of number cards or overhead number tiles with sums equaling 10 or greater. Show children one of the number cards or tiles, such as 4.

How many more to make ten?
(6)

Show second number card or tile, such as 9.

When we add this number, do we have enough to make ten?
(Yes)

How many left over?
(3)

Extension Present number cards or tiles to which 4 through 8 are added to make a sum of 20 or more.

How many more make 20? When we add this number, do we have enough to make twenty? How many left over?

Day 10

Select pairs of number cards or overhead number tiles with sums equaling 10 or greater. Show children one number card or tile, such as 7.

How many more to make ten?
(3)

Show second number card or tile, such as 5.

When we add this number, do we have enough to make ten?
(Yes)

How many left over?
(2)

Extension Present number cards or tiles to which 4 through 8 are added to make a sum of 20 or more.

How many more make 20? When we add this number, do we have enough to make twenty? How many left over?

Ten-Frame Teens

●●●

Small Group Activity

Summary

Children work in pairs using two (2) ten-frames. One child sets LinkerCubes® into two ten-frames to model a fact with a sum greater than ten. The second child estimates the sum. The children write the fact without the answer. Working together, they move cubes to fill one ten-frame and have leftovers in the second ten-frame. Children then write the answer to complete the fact.

Materials

Each pair of children needs

▶ A copy of Ten-Frame Teens, page 80

▶ Twenty (20) LinkerCubes®

Directions

❶ Give each pair of children a copy of Ten-Frame Teens, page 80, and twenty (20) LinkerCubes. Remind children how to show numbers on a ten-frame—always fill the top row first from left to right, then the bottom row from left to right.

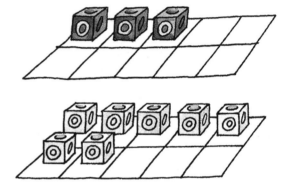

❷ As a whole class activity, model making ten facts like 8 + 3, 7 + 5, 9 + 4, 6 + 6, and 3 + 9. Be sure to record the facts on the board as children model them.

❸ Using the ten-frames on page 80, have children show addends with a sum greater than ten. Children should work in pairs and take turns.

4 Have one child fill the ten frames while keeping them hidden from his or her partner. The child should place at least eleven (11) cubes into the ten-frames making sure to put some cubes in each ten-frame.

5 When the ten-frames are ready, the second child takes a quick look at them and tells what he or she thinks the sum is. The children then work together moving the cubes to check that the correct sum was given.

6 Instruct children repeat the activity several times switching roles each time.

Talk About It

After all children have completed the Ten-Frame Teens activity, page 80, ask questions such as

How much is 9 + 7?
(16)

How do you know?
(Accept all valid responses.)

Ask children to tell their thinking about several facts for which the making ten strategy could be used.

If a child describes using the making-ten strategy ask

How is that like what we were doing with the ten-frames?
(One of the addends is broken into two smaller addends in a way that one of those smaller addends can be used to make ten.)

Extension or Homework

Give children copies of Ten-Frame Teens, page 80, and Ten-Frame Facts, page 81. Ten-Frame Facts provides target sums that can be made in several ways. Children use the two ten-frames to find several facts with the target sums.

Ten-Frame Teens

Use the two ten-frames to show facts with sums greater than ten.

Directions

1. **Player 1** Secretly place some cubes on each of the ten-frames. Be sure to make facts with sums greater than ten.

2. **Player 2** Take a quick look at the ten-frames. Tell what you think is the sum of the cubes in the ten-frames.

3. Together, move the cubes to check the sum.

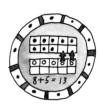

Ten-Frame Facts

Use the two ten-frames from Ten-frame Teens, page 80, and LinkerCubes® to find addends that equal the sum of the numbers in each box.

How many different pairs of addends can you find with a sum equal to each number below?

| 13 | 14 | 15 | 16 | 17 | 18 |

1.

___ + ___ = _____

2.

___ + ___ = _____

3.

___ + ___ = _____

4.

___ + ___ = _____

5.

___ + ___ = _____

6.

___ + ___ = _____

7.

___ + ___ = _____

8.

___ + ___ = _____

9.

___ + ___ = _____

10.

___ + ___ = _____

Making-Ten Strategy

Practice

Work on these sets of practice exercises until children can get each answer within three (3) seconds. Ask children to tell the entire fact rather than just the answer ("7 + 5 = 12," instead of "12"). When children tell the complete fact, it improves their recall. Try presenting the facts in various ways. Ask the children to listen and then reply verbally, or use flash cards and have the children write their facts. Varying the format helps all children focus on the facts.

Talk About It

Ask children to talk about their thinking. Follow up by asking if anyone has a different way to find the answer.

How do you know how many more it takes to make 10?
(Accept all valid responses.)

How do you know how many are left over?
(Accept all valid responses.)

For what other addition facts can this strategy be useful?
(Accept all valid responses.)

What other strategies can be used to help memorize these facts?
(Commutative property, count on, doubles, and near doubles.)

A great question to keep the discussion going is

Does anyone have a different way to find the answer?

Day 1

Show children the number card 9.

How many more to make 10?
(1)

Show the second card, 4.

If we take one from here, how many are left over?
(3)

Continue this activity. Show number cards 8, 7, and 6 in descending order. Repeat questions showing 4 on the second number card each time.

Extension Repeat activity using number cards 19, 18, 17, and 16, adding 4 to each.

How many more to make 20? How many left over?

© Creative Publications 32310

Day 2

Show the number card 9.

How many more to make 10?
(1)

Show the second card, 5.

If we take one from here, how many left over?
(4)

Continue this activity. Show number cards 8, 7, and 6 in descending order. Repeat questions showing number card 5 each time.

Extension Repeat activity using number cards 19, 18, 17, and 16, adding 5 to each.

How many more to make 20? How many left over?

Day 3

Show children the number card 9.

How many more to make 10?
(1)

Show the second card, 6.

If we take one from here, how many left over?
(5)

Continue this activity. Show number cards 8, 7, and 6 in descending order. Repeat questions showing number card 6 each time.

Extension Repeat activity using number cards 19, 18, 17, and 16, adding 6 to each.

How many more to make 20? How many left over?

Day 4

Show children the number cards.

Show the first card, 9.

How many more to make 10?
(1)

Show the second card, 7.

If we take one from here, how many left over?
(6)

What is 10 + 6? (16)

What is 9 + 7? (16)

Continue this activity. Show number cards 8, 7, and 6 in descending order. Repeat questions showing number card 7 each time.

Extension Repeat activity using number cards 19, 18, 17, and 16, adding 7 to each.

How many more to make 20? How many left over?

Day 5

Show the number card 4.

How many more to make 10?
(6)

Show a second card, 8.

If we take one from here, how many left over?
(2)

What is 10 + 2? (12)

What is 4 + 8? (12)

Continue this activity with number cards 3 through 8. Show as many combinations as you feel appropriate.

Extension Repeat activity using number cards from 3 through 8, then show a second number card to make a sum of 20 or greater.

How many more to make 20? How many left over?

Day 6

Present these facts.

7 + 5 (12)	5 + 6 (11)
9 + 3 (12)	6 + 6 (12)
8 + 6 (14)	8 + 5 (13)
6 + 5 (11)	9 + 4 (13)
9 + 6 (15)	6 + 9 (15)
6 + 7 (13)	7 + 7 (14)
5 + 8 (13)	5 + 7 (12)
8 + 4 (12)	7 + 3 (10)
9 + 5 (14)	8 + 7 (15)
7 + 8 (15)	5 + 5 (10)

Extension Present facts with a sum from 20 through 25.

Day 7

Present these facts.

9 + 7 (16)	7 + 7 (14)
6 + 8 (14)	6 + 4 (10)
7 + 4 (11)	9 + 4 (13)
8 + 8 (16)	5 + 7 (12)
5 + 9 (14)	8 + 6 (14)
7 + 6 (13)	6 + 7 (13)
8 + 5 (13)	9 + 5 (14)
9 + 6 (15)	5 + 8 (13)
6 + 5 (11)	7 + 5 (12)
8 + 4 (12)	5 + 6 (11)

Extension Present facts with a sum from 20 through 25.

Day 8

Present these facts.

4 + 8 (12)	6 + 8 (14)
9 + 7 (16)	7 + 6 (13)
5 + 5 (10)	9 + 5 (14)
6 + 9 (15)	4 + 9 (13)
8 + 7 (15)	5 + 9 (14)
4 + 7 (11)	6 + 7 (13)
6 + 4 (10)	8 + 4 (12)
5 + 7 (12)	9 + 6 (15)
9 + 4 (13)	4 + 6 (10)
8 + 8 (16)	6 + 6 (12)

Extension Present facts with a sum from 20 through 25.

Day 9

Show children addition flash cards for sums of 10 or more.

Extension Show children flash cards for sums 0 through 20.

Day 10

Show children addition flash cards for sums of 10 through 20.

Extension Show children flash cards for sums 0 through 20.

Name _____

Addition Chart

+	0	1	2	3	4	5	6	7	8	9	10
0	0	1	2	3	4	5	6	7	8	9	10
1	1	2	3	4	5	6	7	8	9	10	11
2	2	3	4	5	6	7	8	9	10	11	12
3	3	4	5	6	7	8	9	10	11	12	13
4	4	5	6	7	8	9	10	11	12	13	14
5	5	6	7	8	9	10	11	12	13	14	15
6	6	7	8	9	10	11	12	13	14	15	16
7	7	8	9	10	11	12	13	14	15	16	17
8	8	9	10	11	12	13	14	15	16	17	18
9	9	10	11	12	13	14	15	16	17	18	19
10	10	11	12	13	14	15	16	17	18	19	20

Addition Chart

+	0	1	2	3	4	5	6	7	8	9	10
0											
1											
2											
3											
4											
5											
6											
7											
8											
9											
10											

Bibliography

Practice Your Facts. Chicago, Creative Publications, Inc., 1999. These 80-page practice books offer traditional practice on all facts. Levels 1–5.

Holden, Linda, and Micaelia Randolph Brummett. *Understanding Addition & Subtraction.* Chicago, Creative Publications, Inc., 1988. Forty-eight carefully sequenced, reproducible lessons help children make connections between concrete experiences, pictorial representations, and abstract equations. The 128-page binder includes activities using linking cubes and counting chips.

Irvine, Rhea, and Kathryn Walker. *Smart Arithmetic, Grades 1-3.* Chicago, Creative Publications, Inc., 1995. This 96-page teacher resource book helps you guide your children in a thinking approach to computation as they invent their own algorithms. A start-up bank of suggested activities provides experiences in discourse, visual thinking, mental computation, and fact recall.

National Council of Teachers of Mathematics *Standards 2000 Draft.* Reston, Virginia, 2000. This document emphasizes the importance of mastering basic facts. Indeed, fast and accurate recall of basic facts is an essential tool in the mathematical toolkit.

Pittock, Janet, and Ann Roper. *Practice Worth Repeating.* Chicago, Creative Publications, Inc., 1999. Help children keep their fact recall fast and accurate with enjoyable practice. These manageable 32-page books include several engaging practice activities that can be used over and over with the same children.

Ward, Sandra. *Constructing Ideas About Number Combinations.* Chicago, Creative Publications, Inc., 1995. Fourteen one- to five-day explorations help children construct and deepen their understanding of addition and subtraction. Each exploration is clearly presented in an easy to use format and includes reproducible homework. 112 pages.

Larry Leutzinger, author of the *Facts That Last* series, is an associate professor at the University of Northern Iowa and co-director of the Iowa Mathematics and Science Coalition. Dr. Leutzinger's major interests include teaching mental mathematics concepts, including basic facts, to pre-K through fourth grade students. He is actively researching the knowledge and abilities of those students.